TO: _____

_____

_____

YOU'RE A GRANDPARENT

WRITTEN BY M.H. CLARK

ILLUSTRATED BY HIROKO YOSHIMOTO

you're a GRANDPARENT.

WHICH MEANS
EVERYTHING *you are*
MATTERS,
SO VERY MUCH...

BECAUSE
YOU'RE A STORYTELLER.
YOU'RE A TEACHER.
you're a MEMORY KEEPER.

YOU'RE A LISTENER.
YOU'RE A LAUGHER.

YOU'RE MORE *than*
JUST A LITTLE BIT MAGIC.

YOU'RE A MAKER
of DREAMS COME TRUE.

YOU'RE A very GOOD HUGGER.

And SOMEONE TO WHISPER TO.

YOU'RE A BELIEVER
IN WISHES.

YOU SWING SWINGS.
YOU SING SONGS.

and WHEREVER YOU ARE
IS A PLACE to BELONG.

And you're
FULL OF SURPRISES.

YOU CAN MAKE
AN ADVENTURE *from*
an ORDINARY DAY.

YOU'RE SOMEONE
TO PLAY WITH,
and SOMEONE TO STAY WITH.

AND A HAND to HOLD
ALONG THE WAY.

YOU'RE A HIDER,
AND A SEEKER,

AND YOU'RE SILLY,
AND YOU'RE FUN.

And yet,
YOU'RE ALSO WISER
than ALMOST ANYONE.

YOU'RE A READER *of*
just ONE MORE BOOK
BEFORE BED...

And a GIVER OF KISSES

GOOD NIGHT.

AND NO MATTER
WHAT HAPPENS,

YOU ALWAYS KNOW
JUST HOW to make
THINGS RIGHT.

And MOMENTS WITH YOU
ARE SO CHERISHED.

BECAUSE YOU KNOW
WHAT TOGETHERNESS is FOR.

GLUE

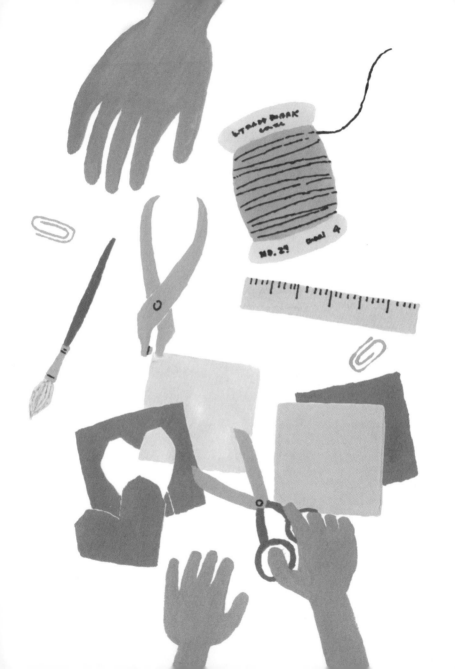

AND AS THE YEARS
CHANGE EACH OF US,
YOU ONLY *matter more.*

BECAUSE
you're a GRANDPARENT.
YOU'RE A CONSTANT.

YOU'RE a GENTLE,
GUIDING STAR.

AND IT'S CLEAR
how VERY MUCH
YOU MEAN,

and JUST HOW
LOVED YOU ARE.

WITH SPECIAL THANKS
TO THE ENTIRE COMPENDIUM FAMILY.

CREDITS:

Written by: M.H. CLARK

Illustrated by: HIROKO YOSHIMOTO

Design & Art Direction by: SARAH FORSTER

Edited by: RUTH AUSTIN

Library of Congress Control Number: 2017942876

ISBN: 978-1-943200-72-6

1st printing. Printed in China with soy inks. A03201709001